Melanin Expressions presents:

I AM <u>Not</u> My Skin!

Affirmations for Melanated Children

Written By: Alesha Edwards

Dedication

This book is dedicated to my three children, Sir Leonard (LJ), Alexandria (Lexi), and Sir Lennox (Pooh-doodle). I thank God for the three of you and the joy you have brought to our family. Each one of you is special and unique. May the three of you always know how loved you are and how special you are. I need you to remember that your worth comes from God and within. Use these affirmations as reminders of who you are and that your potential is uncapped!

This book is also dedicated to every melanated child who has been made to feel less than, like they are not beautiful/handsome, and like their potential is limited based on what others say about them. Remember your self worth comes from within. Use these affirmations as a daily reminder that you are special with unlimited potential to be whatever you want to be!

Melanin children, and adults, our skin is a beautiful addition to who we are. Do not let the world make you feel like you are less than because of your skin color. Do not let the world make you feel that you are only your skin- defined by it! Do not let the world mistreat you because of your beautiful, melanated skin. Celebrate it and celebrate yourself! Embrace it and embrace your future!

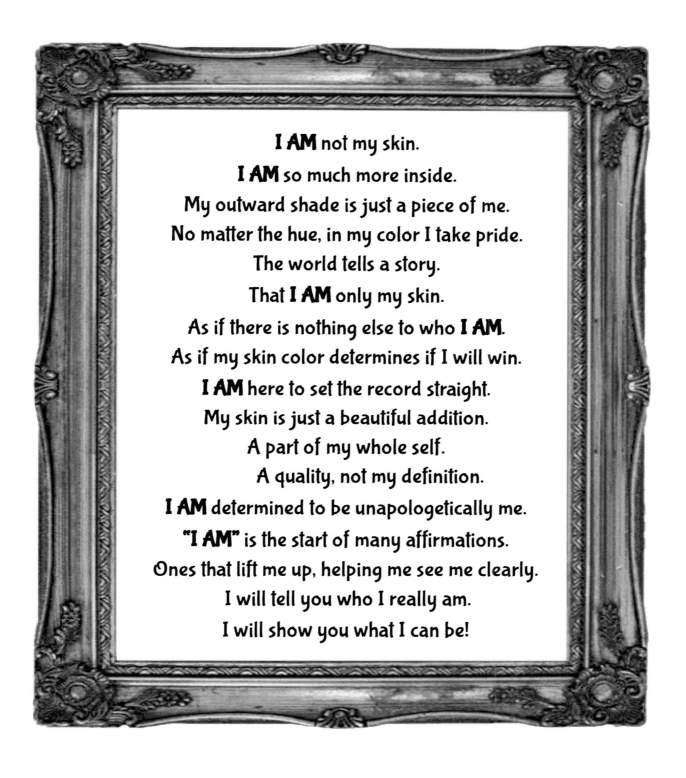

I **AM** not my skin.

I **AM** so much more inside.

My outward shade is just a piece of me.

No matter the hue, in my color I take pride.

The world tells a story.

That I **AM** only my skin.

As if there is nothing else to who I **AM**.

As if my skin color determines if I will win.

I **AM** here to set the record straight.

My skin is just a beautiful addition.

A part of my whole self.

A quality, not my definition.

I **AM** determined to be unapologetically me.

"I **AM**" is the start of many affirmations.

Ones that lift me up, helping me see me clearly.

I will tell you who I really am.

I will show you what I can be!

I AM A LEADER!

Let's start here.

Leading future generations

To their goals, far and near.

I will follow the footsteps,

Of many great women and men.

Continuing the fight for our people.

One that has yet to end.

SOME LEADERS YOU MAY KNOW:

<u>Dr. Martin Luther King Jr.</u>: Baptist minister, activist, and leader in the Civil Rights movement.

<u>Malcolm X</u>: a Muslim minister and activist in the Civil Rights Movement.

<u>Harriet Tubman</u>: former slave, conductor on the Underground Railroad, speaker, and General in the Union Army.

<u>Barack Obama</u>: 44th President, first African American president, and former Senator.

<u>Kamala Harris</u>: 49th Vice President, first African/Asian American Vice President, and former Senator.

SOME LEADERS WHO MAY BE NEW TO YOU:

<u>Medgar Evers:</u> Civil Rights activist, NAACP field secretary for Mississippi, and a WWII Veteran.

<u>Octavious V. Cotto:</u> Civil Rights activist and principal of the Institute for Colored Youth in Philadelphia.

<u>Ruby Bridges:</u> the first African American child to desegregate an all-white school in Louisiana.

<u>Richard Allen:</u> a minister, educator, writer, and founder of the African Methodist Episcopal Church.

<u>Nat Turner:</u> an enslaved preacher who led slaves on a four-day rebellion against their masters on August 21, 1831.

<u>Sojourner Truth:</u> a former slave who escaped and became an abolitionist and women's rights activist.

I AM ARTISTIC!

Creativity runs through my blood.

My imagination runs wild with ideas.

Creating masterpieces guaranteed to be loved!

So many different artists

Came before my time.

Inspiring me to create art of my own.

Expressing myself through art, writing, and music,

sometimes combined.

SOME ARTISTS YOU MAY KNOW:

<u>Langston Hughes</u>: a poet, activist, novelist, playwright, columnist, and known leader of the Harlem Renaissance.

<u>Michael Jackson</u>: singer, songwriter, dancer, and philanthropist. He is dubbed the "King of Pop"!

<u>Prince</u>: singer, songwriter, multi-instrumentalist, record producer, actor, and director.

<u>Jean-Michel Basquiat</u>: a Neo-expressionist artist and one of the most influential artists of the 20th century.

<u>Spike Lee:</u> film director, producer, screenwriter, actor, professor, and creator of *40 Acres and a Mule* production company.

<u>Tyler, the Creator:</u> rapper, singer, songwriter, record producer, actor, visual artist, designer, and comedian.

SOME ARTISTS WHO MAY BE NEW TO YOU:

<u>James Baldwin</u>: a novelist, playwright, essayist, poet, and activist.

<u>Faith Ringgold</u>: a painter, writer, mixed-media sculptor, performance artist, and known for her narrative quilts.

<u>Aaron Douglas</u>: a painter, illustrator, and visual arts educator. He was a major figure in the Harlem Renaissance.

<u>Nina Simone:</u> a singer, songwriter, musician, arranger, and Civil Rights Activist.

<u>George Clinton</u>: a funk musician, singer, songwriter, bandleader, and record producer.

<u>Gordon Parks</u>: a photographer, musician, writer, and film director.

I AM AN ATHLETE!

It is part of my every day.

Sometimes I compete in sports,

Or I am just actively at play.

There have been numerous athletes

Players of the past, some still playing today.

The list of sports they have enjoyed is limitless.

Showing me there is an inner athlete inside waiting to

come out and play!

SOME ATHLETES YOU MAY KNOW:

<u>Kobe Bryant</u>: a professional basketball player for the Los Angeles Lakers.

<u>LeBron James</u>: a professional basketball player for the Cleveland Cavaliers, Miami Heat, then Lakers.

<u>Jackie Robinson</u>: a baseball player for the Brooklyn Dodgers and 1st African-American to play in a Major League.

<u>Serena Williams</u>: a professional tennis player and former "Number 1 (No.1)" in women's single tennis.

<u>Muhammad Ali</u>: a professional boxer, activist, entertainer, poet, and philanthropist. He is regarded as the greatest heavyweight boxer of all time.

<u>Simon Biles</u>: an artistic gymnast with 30 Olympic and World Championship medals.

SOME ATHLETES WHO MAY BE NEW TO YOU:

<u>Wilma Rudolph</u>: a sprinter who became a world-record Olympic Champion and international sports icon.

<u>Althea Gibson</u>: a tennis player and professional golfer. One of the first Black athletes to cross the color line in international tennis. The first African-American to win a Grand Slam title in tennis.

<u>Jesse Owens</u>: a track and field athlete and four-time gold medalist in the Olympic Games.

<u>Cullen Jones</u>: a freestyle swimmer, Olympic gold medalist, and holds the record in the 4x100-meter freestyle relay.

<u>Sheryl Swoopes</u>: a former professional basketball player, first signed to the WNBA, and WNBA all-star.

<u>Arthur Ashe</u>: professional tennis player with 3 Grand Slam singles titles. The only black man to win the singles at Wimbledon, US Open, and the Australian Open. The first black player selected to the US Davis Cup Team.

I AM VALUABLE!

I have so much worth.

My value is more than American history tells.

A precious diamond since my birth.

My value and shine improves the world.

Making it better one day at a time.

My value demands respect.

You can't steal my value, it's MINE!

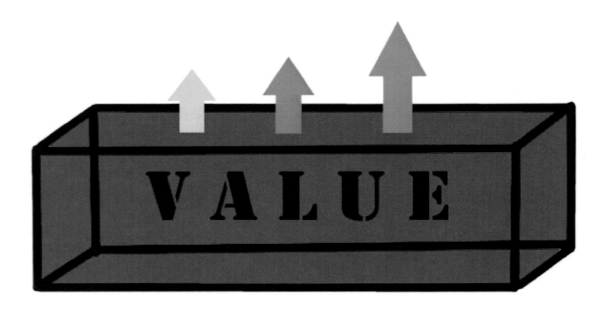

SOME VALUABLE PEOPLE YOU MAY KNOW:

<u>George Washington Carver</u>: an agricultural scientist and inventor. He is responsible for over 300 products created from peanuts. He was the most prominent black scientist of the 20th century.

<u>Madame C.J. Walker</u>: an entrepreneur, philanthropist, and activist. She is best known for her hair product inventions that made her the first female self-made millionaire.

<u>Lonnie Johnson</u>: an inventor, aerospace engineer, and entrepreneur. He is known for the invention of the Super Soaker and Nerf gun. He also worked with the US Air Force and for NASA.

<u>Garrett Morgan</u>: an inventor, businessman, and community leader, best known for his invention of the traffic light and smoke hood.

SOME VALUABLE PEOPLE YOU MAY NOT KNOW:

<u>Lewis Lattimer</u>: an inventor and patent draftsman. He is best known for inventing the air conditioner, carbon filaments for light bulbs, and an improved toilet system for railroad cars.

<u>Marie Van Brittan Brown</u>: a nurse and innovator. She is best known for inventing the video home security system.

<u>Otis Boykin</u>: an inventor and engineer. He invented electrical resistors used in missiles and pacemakers.

<u>Lisa Gelobter</u>: a computer scientist, entrepreneur, and credited with developing the animation for GIFS.

<u>Alfred Cralle</u>: a businessman and inventor of the ice cream scoop.

I AM POWERFUL!

Power lies within my muscles.

My power is endless.

It gets me through any struggle.

I AM more than just my skin,

But please don't be confused.

We always come together to fight against injustice and abuse.

Like the black fist, we are stronger united.

Melanin Power exists all around the world.

This power lies within every melanin man, woman, boy, and girl.

SOME POWERFUL PEOPLE YOU MAY KNOW:

<u>Frederick Douglass:</u> an American social reformer, abolitionist, orator, writer, and statesmen. He escaped from slavery and became a national leader in the abolitionist movement and famous for his antislavery writings.

<u>Booker T. Washington:</u> an educator, author, orator, and adviser to several presidents of the United States. Found the Tuskegee Institute and the National Negro Business League.

<u>Rosa Parks:</u> she refused to give up her seat on a segregated bus, which led to a boost in the Civil Rights Movement and earned her the title of "the first lady of civil rights" and "the mother of the freedom movement".

<u>Shirley Chisholm:</u> a politician, educator, and author. The first African American woman elected to Congress and the first African American to run for president.

SOME POWERFUL PEOPLE YOU MAY NOT KNOW:

<u>Martin Delany:</u> an abolitionist, journalist, physician, soldier, and writer. He is said to be the first supporter of Black Nationalism. He was also the first African American Field Officer in the United States Army.

<u>Coretta Scott King:</u> an author, activist, and Civil Rights leader. After the assassination of her husband Dr. Martin Luther King Jr., she continued his legacy and created her own legacy in the fight to end racial injustice.

<u>Benjamin O. Davis Jr. :</u> a United States Air Force General and commander of the WWII Tuskegee Airmen. He was the first black Brigadier General in the US Air Force.

<u>Fred Hampton:</u> an activist and revolutionary socialist. Chairman of the Illinois chapter of the Black Panther Party (B.P.P.) and deputy chairmen of the national Black Panther Party.

I AM INTELLIGENT!

I have a big, beautiful brain.

Always seeking to learn more.

Information I yearn to gain.

So many smart, melanated people

Past and present- they've existed on this planet.

I am just one of many.

My mind's potential is growing.

I don't take it for granted.

SOME INTELLIGENT PEOPLE YOU MAY KNOW:

<u>Angela Davis:</u> a political activist, philosopher, professor, and author. She is a founding member of the Committees of Correspondence for Democracy and Socialism.

<u>W.E.B. DuBois:</u> a sociologist, socialist, historian, Civil Rights activist, father of Pan-Africanism, author, writer, and editor. He believed all people of African descent should work together towards ending prejudice and inequality.

<u>James Baldwin:</u> a novelist, playwright, poet, activist, and known for exploring racial and class distinctions.

<u>Amanda Gorman:</u> a poet, activist, and first National Youth Poet Laureate. The youngest poet to perform at a Presidential Inauguration (in 2021). Her piece focused on race, oppression, and marginalization within the U.S.A.

SOME INTELLIGENT PEOPLE YOU MAY NOT KNOW:

<u>Mary Frances Berry:</u> a historian, writer, lawyer, activist, and professor who focuses on African American history, regarding U.S. constitutional and legal rights.

<u>Ta-Nehisi Coates:</u> a journalist and author. Well-known for writing about social, cultural, and political issues specifically involving white supremacy and African Americans.

<u>Kimberle W. Crenshaw:</u> a lawyer, philosopher, Civil Rights advocate, professor, and leading scholar in Critical Race Theory.

<u>Edmond Keller:</u> a political science professor and former director of the UCLA Globalization Research Center-Africa.

I AM A SURVIVOR!

Hard times don't make me quit.

I keep pushing forward.

Showing the world I've got grit!

Sometimes the waters get rough.

Life's waves can cause much pain.

But no matter what I go through,

I stay strong and hopeful through the storm and rain.

SOME SURVIVORS YOU MAY KNOW:

<u>Tarana Burke:</u> an activist from The Bronx, New York who started the Me Too Movement. She has used her platform to help other women survivors stand up for themselves and let their voices be heard.

<u>Mamie Till:</u> an American educator and activist. The mother of Emmett Till; he was brutally murdered while on vacation in the South. She sparked a new wave in the Civil Rights Movement as she held her son's funeral with an open casket so that "the world would see what they did to her baby."

<u>Maya Angelou:</u> a poet and Civil Rights activist. She endured a lot of abuse and pain as a young girl and went mute for 5 years as she believed her voice brought death upon her family. She endured through this and many other trials as a young adult to become an award winning poet, author, and activist.

SOME SURVIVORS YOU MAY NOT KNOW:

<u>Henry "Box" Brown:</u> a slave whose wife and children were sold by his master to another plantation. Tired of the abuse, he escaped slavery by shipping himself in a 3 ft. box up North to abolitionists. The trip took 27 hours, traveling in the box by boat, train, and wagon.

<u>Claudia Gordon:</u> the first deaf Black female attorney in the United States. She did not let her disability stop her from achieving her goals.

<u>Isaac Woodard:</u> a WWII Veteran who was attacked and beaten by police, while in uniform, on his way home from serving his country. The attack left him blind and sparked action in the Civil Rights movement.

I AM LOVED!

For who I am.

By those that know me.

Loved by friends and teachers.

Loved by blood and extended family.

Even though being loved by others

Is what we all desire and need.

The best type of love

Is for me to love me!

Love me for my good qualities.

Even love myself for mistakes made.

Loving my growth over time.

Self-love is an empowerment parade.

I AM...

I AM...

I AM...

There are many other affirmations.

That apply to my daily life.

I AM worthy, faults and all,

My worth is determined through my own eyes.

I AM melanated and beautiful

My uniqueness should be celebrated.

Not made fun of, hated on,

Or ridiculously duplicated.

I AM my ancestor's child.

My people have been through many storms.

Pain is a constant part of life,

For us, hatred must no longer feel like a norm.

I AM a dreamer, hopeful for the future.

I AM grateful for everything **I AM** and possess.

I AM forgiving to those who hurt me.

I AM evolving into the version of myself that is the best.

AN AFFIRMATION CHALLENGE:

I challenge you today

To make a promise that will last a lifetime.

Start your days looking in the mirror

Say an affirmation that will carry you to bedtime.

Love yourself daily

No matter what the world may say.

Know how truly special you are

And never let your confidence sway.

You are more than just your skin

More than America wants you, I, or the world to know.

Never stop your shine for anyone!

Never let anyone stop your show!

What is an affirmation?

An **affirmation** is a word or phrase repeated to oneself to declare a certain belief or feeling.
Affirmations help a person change their mindset and become the person they truly wish to be.
Affirmations motivate, inspire, and encourage us to take action and realize our goals.

Affirmations require you to:

★ State a fact.

★ Believe what you say.

★ Support yourself and those around you.

★ Encourage one another.

★ Stand strong in your beliefs.

What affirmations speak to you most?

Can you think of other affirmations to tell yourself daily in the mirror?

Write them below.

Made in United States
North Haven, CT
01 March 2023